clutter
free

WHAT JESUS HAS TO SAY ABOUT YOUR STUFF

the bible study

By Kathi Lipp &
Jennifer Daly, M.B.A.

Clutter Free Bible Study
ISBN-10: 1-944434-00-3
ISBN-13: 978-1-944434-00-7

All Scripture quotations are marked with the version they are taken from and
pulled from https://www.biblegateway.com.

Published in conjunction with Harvest House Publishing and Kathi Lipp, LLC.

Welcome, friends, to
Clutter Free the Bible Study!

To get the most out of this study, we recommend three things:

1. Have an open heart and willing spirit to hear what God wants to teach you.

2. Prior to your group meeting, pre-read the suggested chapters of Clutter Free and complete the discussion questions.

3. Have FUN getting rid of everything that has been holding you back from your life's purpose!

Overview

Session 1 – Part 1:   Uncovering the Costs of Clutter
Chapters 1 – 4

Session 2 – Part 2:   Why We Buy Stuff
Chapters 5 - 8

Session 3 – Part 3:   Why We Keep Stuff
Chapters 9 – 13

Session 4 – Part 4:   Why We Keep Stuff
Chapters 14 – 18

Session 5 – Part 5:   How to Get Rid of Stuff
Chapters 19 – 21

Session 6 – Part 6:   How to Get Rid of Stuff
Chapters 22 – 25

Uncovering the Costs of Clutter

At Home

Read chapters 1-4 and complete the following reflection questions:

1. Clutter is keeping you from the peace you desire in your home. What is currently keeping you from dealing with your clutter?

2. What is one routine you could put into place this week to get you "closer to the clutter-free existence you long for"?

3. What organizational systems do you currently have in place?

Video Notes

Jesus said to him, "If you wish to be complete,
go and sell your possessions and give to the poor,
and you shall have treasure in heaven;
and come, follow Me."

Matthew 19:21 (NAS)

Diving Deeper- Group Discussion

1. As Kathi both discussed in the book and video, which of the "everyday actions that cause clutter" do you identify with the most and why?

2. Can the "American Dream" and God's dream for your life be the same?

3. Do you think clutter in the physical sense has anything to do with the health of your spiritual life?

4. Read Matthew 19:21.

> Jesus said to him, "If you wish to be complete, go and sell your possessions and
> give to the poor, and you shall have treasure in heaven; and come, follow Me."
> **Matthew 19:21** (NAS)

How do you think this verse relates to the clutter in our life?

5. Kathi says, "Clutter builds a barrier between us and the rest of the world." (page 33). The Bible commands us to "love one another" (John 13:34 NIV). In what ways does clutter currently keep you from fulfilling God's command?

6. What is one thing God has called you to do however you have not been able to follow Him because of your clutter?

Why We Buy Stuff

At Home

Read chapters 5-8 and complete the following reflection questions:

1. What do you think it would feel like to walk through a store, walk out without a purchase, and still feel satisfied?

2. Reflecting on the ways in which fear, guilt, and shame have contributed to your clutter, which one is your weakest area? What strategies can you implement to begin shifting this way of thinking?

3. What kind of impact do you think decluttering will have on your family? What are some ways you can get them to participate?

Video Notes

> "I know how to live on almost nothing or with everything. I have learned the secret of living in every situation, whether it is with a full stomach or empty, with plenty or little. For I can do everything through Christ, who gives me strength."
>
> **Philippians 4:12-13 (NLV)**

Diving Deeper- Group Discussion

1. This week you read and Kathi spoke about "why we buy stuff". Read Hebrews 13:5.

> "Keep your life free from love of money, and be content with what you have,
> for he has said, "I will never leave you nor forsake you."
> **Hebrews 13:5** (ESV)

Why is it so hard to live clutter free in this day and age?

2. Read Philippians 4:12-13.

> "I know how to be brought low, and I know how to abound. In any and every
> circumstance, I have learned the secret of facing plenty and hunger,
> abundance and need. I can do all things through him who strengthens me."
> **Phillippians 4:12-13** (ESV)

What is "the secret of being content" look like as a Christian?

3. Kathi believes, "Shame says, "I am defective. I need to prove to the world that I'm not."
   Read Hebrews 12:2 and then Psalm 34:4-5.

> "looking to Jesus, the founder and perfecter of our faith, who for the joy that
> was set before him endured the cross, despising the shame, and is seated at
> the right hand of the throne of God."
> **Hebrews 12:2** (ESV)

> "I sought the Lord, and he answered me
> and delivered me from all my fears.
> Those who look to him are radiant,
> and their faces shall never be ashamed."
> **Psalm 34:4-5** (ESV)

What does God say about our shame?

4. Read Isaiah 61:7.

> "Instead of your shame there shall be a double portion;
> instead of dishonor they shall rejoice in their lot;
> therefore in their land they shall possess a double portion;
> they shall have everlasting joy."
> **Isaiah 61:7** (ESV)

Instead of shame, what does God offer us?

5. Of the three triggers that Kathi discusses that leads us to clutter, which one do you most identify with?

> "To you, O Lord, I lift up my soul.
> O my God, in you I trust; let me not be put to shame;
> let not my enemies exult over me.
> Indeed, none who wait for you shall be put to shame;
> they shall be ashamed who are wantonly treacherous."
> **Psalm 25:1-3** (ESV)

How can Psalms 25:1-3 change our attitude about these triggers?

6. Have you had a time when you felt you would miss out if you didn't make a purchase right then? How does Matthew 10:16 encourage us to respond to this type of situation?

> "Behold, I am sending you out as sheep in the midst of wolves, so be wise as serpents and innocent as doves."
> **Matthew 10:16** (ESV)

Why We Keep Stuff, Part A

At Home

Read chapters 9-13 and complete the following reflection questions:

1. How has clutter stolen your peace?

2. Reflecting on Psalm 56:3-4, how can you feel secure in God as you declutter? Moving forward, how do you think you will feel getting rid of your "security blankets"?

> "When I am afraid, I put my trust in you. In god, whose word I praise, in God I trust; I shall not be afraid. What can flesh do to me?"
> **Psalm 56:3-4** (ESV)

3. What familial patterns have set you up to struggle with clutter, and are you perpetuating the clutter cycle for others?

Video Notes

Do not store up for yourselves treasures on earth, where moth
and rust destroy, and where thieves break in and steal.
But store up for yourselves treasures in heaven, where neither
moth nor rust destroys, and where thieves do not break in or steal;
for where your treasure is, there your heart will be also.

Matthew 6:19-21 (NLT)

Diving Deeper- Group Discussion

1. Read 2 Timothy 1:7.

> "for God gave us a spirit not of fear but of power and love and self-control."
> **2 Timothy 1:7 (ESV)**

What key word in 2 Timothy 1:7 can help us the next time we have a "just in case" buying mentality? How else can this verse help us get away from being rooted in fear?

2. Kathi mentions "things do not equal love". Read Matthew 6:19-21.

> "Do not lay up for yourselves treasures on earth, where moth and rust[a] destroy and where thieves break in and steal, 20 but lay up for yourselves treasures in heaven, where neither moth nor rust destroys and where thieves do not break in and steal. 21 For where your treasure is, there your heart will be also."
> **Matthew 6:19-21** (ESV)

In what ways can we transform an item we have kept because "so and so gave it to me" from an object to a reflection of God's love?

3. Do you have items at home that seem to shuffle from place to place because they have no specific home to land? Pick one area that seems to collect un-homed items the most and write out a practical way you can start clearing that space.

4. Besides your home having clutter, do you ever feel like you are fighting mental clutter? How does 1 Corinthians 14:40 help us in both senses?

> "But all things should be done decently and in order."
> **1 Corinthians 14:40** (ESV)

5. God has a purpose for each of us. What does Ephesians 1:17-18 say that will help us better understand that purpose?

> "that the God of our Lord Jesus Christ, the Father of glory, may give you the Spirit of wisdom and of revelation in the knowledge of him, having the eyes of your hearts enlightened, that you may know what is the hope to which he has called you, what are the riches of his glorious inheritance in the saints,"
> **Ephesians 1:17-18** (ESV)

Why We Keep Stuff, Part B

At Home

Read chapters 14-18 and complete the following reflection questions:

1. Is there anyone in your family that you feel will hinder your clutter busting process? What are some ways you can make decluttering easier for everyone?

2. We need to make room in our life for what is growing and working. What are some "end of life" decisions that you need to make to move forward? What is currently making these decisions difficult?

3. Make a list of what is truly important to you. What can you do this week to intentionally make room for those things?

Video Notes

I am leaving you with a gift--peace of mind and heart.
And the peace I give is a gift the world cannot give.
So don't be troubled or afraid.

John 14:27 (NLV)

Diving Deeper- Group Discussion

1. Read John 3:18.

> "Whoever believes in him is not condemned, but whoever does not
> believe is condemned already, because he has not believed in the
> name of the only Son of God."
> **John 3:18** (ESV)

What practical guides does this verse give us for lovingly helping someone else with their clutter?

2. When thinking "but I have so much invested in it", Kathi reveals this is a great time to come to terms with endings and look to your future. How does Job 8:7 encourage us in this?

> "And though your beginning was small,
> your latter days will be very great."
> **Job 8:7** (ESV)

3. What can we learn from Matthew 6:26 (specifically the NIV or NLT translations) in regards to the "what if I don't have enough" mentality?

> "Look at the birds of the air; they do not sow or reap or store away in barns, and yet your heavenly Father feeds them. Are you not much more valuable than they?"
> **Matthew 6:26** (NIV)

4. Fill in this blank with a current fear: If I don't buy _____, I won't _____. Read John 14:27.

> "Peace I leave with you; my peace I give you. I do not give to you as the world gives. Do not let your hearts be troubled and do not be afraid."
> **John 14:27** (NIV)

What is God saying in this verse that is so hard for us to grasp and why?

· Week 4 ·

Why We Keep Stuff, Part B

5. Do you know what God has called you to do? Read Proverbs 20:5.

> "The purposes of a person's heart are deep waters,
> but one who has insight draws them out."
> **Proverbs 20:5** (NIV)

How does this verse relate to clutter and God's plan for your life?

6. Now that Kathi has walked us through the "whys" behind clutter, can you identify the root cause of your clutter?

· ·

Why We Keep Stuff, Part B

How to Get Rid of Stuff, Part A

At Home

Read chapters 19-21 and complete the following reflection questions:

1. After reading about "the secret sauce of clutter management," how do you feel about this mind shift? How will it help you on your decluttering journey?

2. How do you feel about getting rid of 2000 things this year?

3. What will be the hardest part about decluttering your wardrobe? How do you feel when you think about letting go of these items?

Video Notes

> Give, and you will receive. Your gift will return to you in full - pressed down, shaken together to make room for more, running over, and poured into your lap. The amount you give will determine the amount you get back."
>
> **Luke 6:38, NLV**

Diving Deeper- Group Discussion

1. When we honor what is important to us, who else are we honoring according to Proverbs 3:9?

> "Honor the Lord with your wealth
> and with the best part of everything you produce."
> **Proverbs 3:9** (NLT)

Does this make you think differently about the items you want to keep?

2. Read Matthew 6:24.

> "No one can serve two masters. For you will hate one and love the other;
> you will be devoted to one and despise the other.
> You cannot serve God and be enslaved to money."
> **Matthew 6:24** (NLT)

Have you ever struggled with God on keeping something you know He wants you to pass along? What are we choosing when we keep that item?

3. Take a few minutes to fill in the blanks to get a great start on your 2000 things challenge:

    1. Name your friend: _____

    2. Pick your room to start: _____

    3. What's your plan? _____

    4. How can you be flexible? _____

    5. What are your ground rules? _____

4. What will you do with your clutter? Read Luke 12:33-34.

> "Sell your possessions and give to those in need. This will store up treasure
> for you in heaven! And the purses of heaven never get old or develop holes.
> Your treasure will be safe; no thief can steal it and no moth can destroy it.
> Wherever your treasure is, there the desires of your heart will also be."
> **Luke 12:33-34** (NLT)

What are the best options in your community for donating or selling?

5. Is having the mindset that "keeping items we don't need is selfish" helpful? What does Luke 6:38 and Proverbs 11:24-25 say about this concept?

> "Give, and you will receive. Your gift will return to you in full—pressed down, shaken together to make room for more, running over, and poured into your lap. The amount you give will determine the amount you get back."
> **Luke 6:38** (NLT)

> "One person gives freely, yet gains even more; another withholds unduly, but comes to poverty. A generous person will prosper; whoever refreshes others will be refreshed."
> **Proverbs 11:24-25** (NIV)

How to Get Rid of Stuff, Part B

At Home

Read chapters 22-25 and complete the following reflection questions:

1. We generally think of doing without as a negative thing. Can you think of a positive way you and your family can do without?

2. How much is your enough? How will you know and what will you gain from having "enough"?

3. After reading this book, how do you feel about your clutter? What progress have you made so far, and what steps will you take as you continue this decluttering journey?

Video Notes

Philip said, "Lord, show us the Father and that
will be enough for us."

John 14:8, NIV

Diving Deeper- Group Discussion

1. Kathi gives us four principles to guide us through our decluttering; Use it up, Wear it out, Make Do and Do Without. Of these four, which one could you commit to starting with and in what room?

2. "Enough is a beautiful thing." Read John 14:8.

> "Philip said, "Lord, show us the Father and that will be enough for us."
> **John 14:8** (NIV)

If all you had was God, would it be enough? What would you miss? Could you live without those things?

3. Kathi provides us with examples of 50 items we could "get rid of today" in the book and several examples in the video. What are 5 items you can commit to getting rid of in the next 24 hours?

1. _____

2. _____

3. _____

4. _____

5. _____

4. What are two ways that you can keep items from coming in to your home?

5. Do you believe that God has a purpose for your life? Read Jeremiah 29:11.

> "For I know the plans I have for you," says the Lord. "They are plans for good
> and not for disaster, to give you a future and a hope."
> **Jeremiah 29:11** (NLT)

Do you believe clutter is getting in the way of God's call on your life?
Are you willing to clear the clutter in every sense?

My friend,

This is my heart's desire: That you know God's great call on your life and that you can clear the clutter to be the true world-changer He has called you to be!

- Kathi

Thank you.

Books from Kathi Lipp

The Cure for the "Perfect" Life

You know the expectations are unreasonable- even unreachable.

Meet Kathi, a disguised perfectionist always looking to put everyone else's needs above her own, and Cheri, a formerly confused and exhausted poster girl for playing it safe. They've struggled just like you–and found the cure. At last, you'll exchange outdated views of who you should be for a clearer vision of who you are in Christ.

The truth is you don't have to be perfect!

The Get Yourself Organized Project

Finally, an organizational book for women who have given up trying to be Martha Stewart but still desire some semblance of order in their lives.

Full of helpful tips and abundant good humor, *The Get Yourself Organized Project* is for those who want to spend their time living and enjoying life rather than organizing their sock drawer. Great for those that have done *Clutter Free* and are ready to organize the stuff they've decided to keep.

The Husband Project

Do you feel like your marriage has gone from "I do" to "What did I do?" Recapture the romance that made you and your husband fall in love in the first place.

The Husband Project provides 21 days of fun activities to show love and honor to your husband. It is 21 days of purposeful but simple ways to put the spark back into your marriage.

Made in the USA
Las Vegas, NV
06 September 2021